In the Night Garden...™

Annual 2009

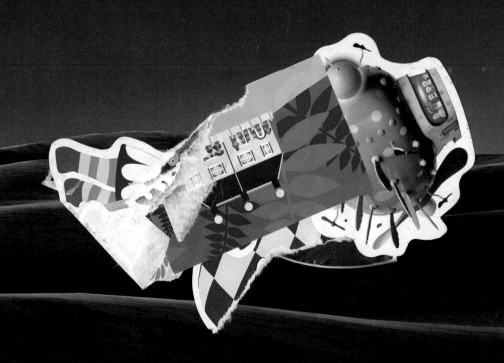

The night is black,
And the stars are bright,
And the sea is dark and deep,
And someone I know,
Is safe and snug,
And drifting off to sleep.

Round and round,
A little boat,
No bigger than your hand,
Out on the ocean,
Far away from land.

Take the little sail down,
Light the little light.
This is the way to the
Garden in the night...

Once upon a time in the Night Garden...™

------------------------ came to play.

Write your name and draw a picture.

Who's here?

Makka Pakka

pages 12-21

Agga pang!

Daisy doo!

Upsy Daisy

pages 22-31

Igglepiggle

pages 32-41

Tombliboos

Pontipines

Put a photo of yourself here.

Igglepiggle, iggle onk, we're going **to catch...**

...the **Ninky Nonk.**

Oh **look,**

it's the

Ninky Nonk!

Follow the Ninky Nonk's
trail with your finger...

All aboard the

Ninky Nonk.

Get ready for a bouncy ride!

Or shall we catch...

Colour the
Ninky Nonk.

...the **Pinky Ponk!**

Oh look, it's the
Pinky Ponk.
Hello **Pinky Ponk!**

Let's make
the Pinky Ponk.
Ask an adult to help you.
Using tracing paper,
transfer the picture onto
a piece of thick card.
Colour it and
cut it out.

Here's Makka Pakka!

Makka Pakka
Akka wakka
Mikka makka moo.

Makka Pakka
Appa yakka
Ikka akka ooo.

Hum dum
Agga pang
Ing ang ooo.

Makka Pakka
Akka wakka
Mikka makka moo!

Count all the stones.
Write the number here.

5

Now colour these stones
for Makka Pakka.

12

Hello Makka Pakka

Parp! Parp!
Makka Pakka loves his trumpet.

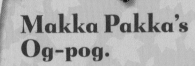

Makka Pakka's Og-pog.

Makka Pakka loves to wash things.

What would you like Makka Pakka to wash? Draw a picture here.

Makka Pakka and the Runaway Og-pog!

Once upon a time in the Night Garden, Makka Pakka came to play.

Hello Makka Pakka!

Makka Pakka was out in the garden, pushing his Og-pog.

Makka Pakka!

Follow the Og-pog BOUNCING along, with your finger or a pencil!

Makka Pakka stopped.
Do you know what he saw?
Stones!
Makka Pakka decided to
clean all the stones.

Splish-splosh-splat!

While Makka Pakka was cleaning the stones, something
happened. His Og-pog rolled away!

Oh dear.

Quick Makka Pakka!
Catch the Og-pog!

Makka Pakka
hurried after
his Og-pog.

Who's here?
The Tombliboos!
Hello Tombliboos.

Quick Tombliboos
– catch the Og-pog!

**Tombliboo!
Tombliboo!**

Who's here?
Igglepiggle!

Quick Igglepiggle
– catch the Og-pog!

Follow the Og-pog
ROLLING along, with
your finger or a pencil!

Who's here?
Upsy Daisy!

Quick Upsy Daisy
– catch the Og-pog!

**Colour all the garden
flowers you can see.**

Upsy Daisy!

Just then the Pontipines
came out of their house.
Mrs Pontipine looked
through her binoculars.

Mi-mi-mi-mi-mi-mi-mi-mi-mi-mi!

And what do you think she saw?

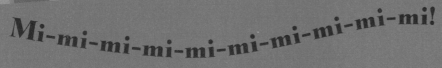

Was it Upsy Daisy?
Was it Igglepiggle?
Was it the Tombliboos?
Was it Makka Pakka?

It was all the friends, chasing
the runaway Og-pog!
What a funny sight!

The Pontipines wanted to
catch the runaway Og-pog too!

Now everyone was chasing
the Og-pog!

Not quite everyone.
Where are the children,
Mr and Mrs Pontipine?

Follow the Og-pog
SWOOSHING along, with
your finger or a pencil!

The teeny tiny Pontipine children were at the very top of a pile of stones.

They pushed... and they pushed.

Crash!

A big stone fell down. The big stone rolled in front of the runaway Og-pog. The Og-pog stopped.

Find all the Pontipine children and colour them.

Mi-mi-mi-mi-mi-mi-mi-mi-mi-mi!

Wasn't that clever of the Pontipine children?

Makka Pakka!

A happy Makka Pakka blew his trumpet.

Makka Pakka has his Og-pog back.
Isn't that a pip?

Now join the dots to help Makka Pakka see his Og-pog.

Parp! Parp!

Follow the trail to the end.

Go to sleep, Makka Pakka.

Colour the picture. Can you remember the story?

Makka Pakka is fast asleep, dreaming about his runaway Og-pog.

21

Here's Upsy Daisy!

Upsy Daisy! Here I come,
I'm the only Upsy one!
I'm the only Daisy too -
Ipsy Upsy Daisy doo!

Upsy Daisy has a favourite thing. Draw over the dots to see what it is.

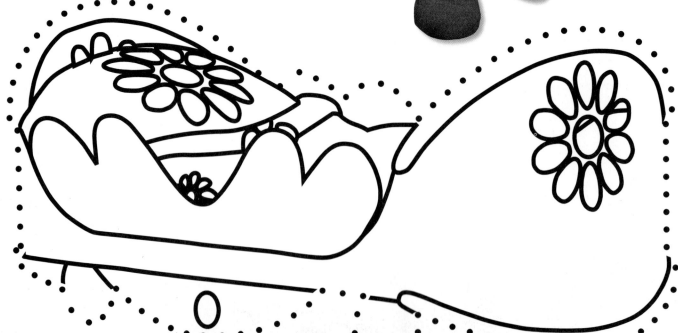

22

Hello Upsy Daisy

Upsy Daisy loves her megaphone.
Who do you think Upsy Daisy
is going to sing to?

Draw Upsy Daisy's
friend here.

Upsy Daisy's
Big
Loud
Sing-song!

Once upon a time in the Night Garden,
Upsy Daisy came to play.

Today Upsy Daisy was singing.

Upsy Daisy...
Upsy Daaaiiiisy...

It was a lovely, loud song.

Mi-mi-mi-mi-mi-
mi-mi-mi-mi-mi!

The Pontipines came out of their house.

Oh dear.
The Pontipines didn't like Upsy Daisy's singing!

The Pontipines hurried back into their house, and shut the front door.

Upsy Daisy was still singing her song.
It was a lovely, loud song.

**Upsy Daisy...
Upsy Daaaiiiisy...**

The Pontipines came out of their house again!

Mi-mi-mi-mi-mi-mi-mi-mi-mi-mi!

Oh dear. The Pontipines still didn't like Upsy Daisy's singing!

Brrrrrring-brrrrrring!

The trubliphone was ringing.

Upsy Daisy answered the trubliphone. But Upsy Daisy didn't know who it was.

Mi-mi-mi-mi-mi-mi-mi-mi-mi-mi!

Upsy Daisy decided to carry on with her singing.

**Upsy Daisy...
Upsy Daaaiiiisy...**

**Mi-mi-mi-mi-mi-
mi-mi-mi-mi-mi!**

said the Pontipines. They hurried back into their house and shut the door.

Colour the Pinky Ponk.

The Pinky Ponk was coming!
Who was riding in it?

Makka Pakka was riding in the Pinky Ponk.

Upsy Daisy sang her lovely
loud song again, especially for
Makka Pakka.

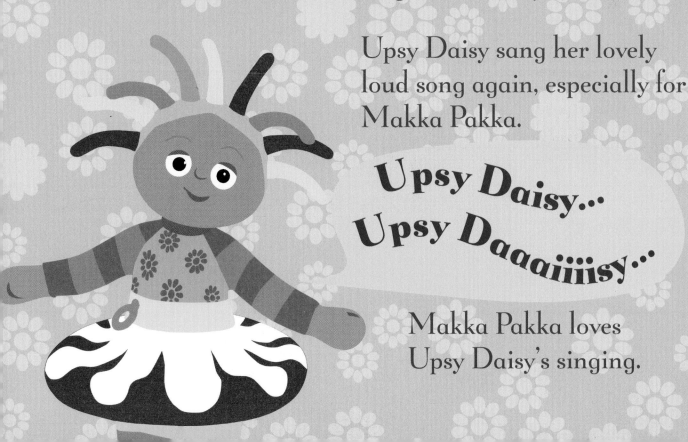

Upsy Daisy...
Upsy Daaaiiiisy...

Makka Pakka loves
Upsy Daisy's singing.

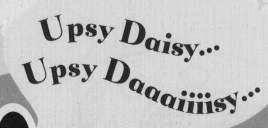

**Upsy Daisy...
Upsy Daaaiiiisy...**

Makka Pakka
blew his trumpet.

What a good idea!

Upsy Daisy sang and Makka
Pakka played his trumpet.

**Parp!
Parp!
Parp!**

Brrrrrring-brrrrrrring!

The trubliphone
was ringing again!

Mi-mi-mi-mi-mi-mi-mi-mi-mi-mi!

It was the Pontipines calling.

The Pontipines liked the new song.

Everybody loved the big loud sing-song!

Isn't that a pip?

Upsy Daisy's megaphone.

Let's make a picture of Upsy Daisy's megaphone! Ask an adult to help you.

You will need: old magazines, and glue.

Using tracing paper, transfer the picture onto a piece of thick card. Tear off small pieces of pretty coloured paper and glue them onto the megaphone.

Go to sleep, Upsy Daisy.

Colour all the daisies while Upsy Daisy sleeps.

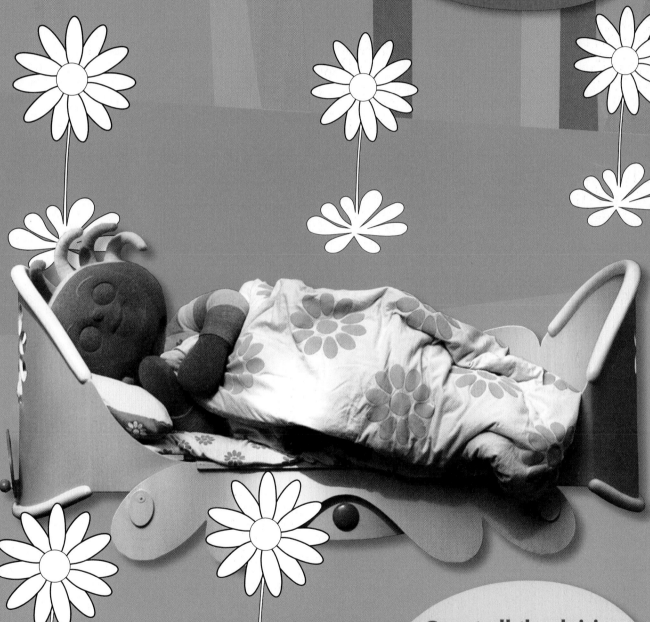

Count all the daisies. Write the number here.

5

Here's Igglepiggle.

Let's colour the
stepping stones.

Yes - my name is Igglepiggle,
Igglepiggle-niggle-wiggle-diggle!
Yes - my name is Igglepiggle
Igglepiggle-niggle-wiggle-woo!

Hello Igglepiggle!

Igglepiggle loves his blan~~
and he loves his f~~

Upsy Daisy is Igglepiggle's
very good friend.

Draw a picture of
your friend here.

Igglepiggle
and the **mucky patch!**

Once upon a time in the Night Garden,
Igglepiggle came to play.

Hello Igglepiggle.

Igglepiggle was dancing.
Igglepiggle danced all around
the garden.

Igglepiggle saw his friend, Makka Pakka.

Hello Makka Pakka!

Makka Pakka!

Igglepiggle danced through the trees, and along the path. Where else?

Onto the bridge!

Ting-a-ling-ling! Dinky-ding-ding!

What lovely music the bridge made when Igglepiggle danced on it!

So Igglepiggle danced on the bridge again.

What fun!

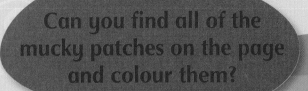

Can you find all of the mucky patches on the page and colour them?

Igglepiggle was so happy, he did a special happy dance.

And... oh dear. Igglepiggle fell down!

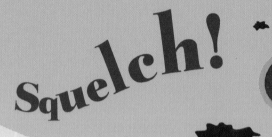

Squelch!

What was that, on Igglepiggle's tummy? It was a mucky patch, from where he fell down. Igglepiggle touched his tummy.

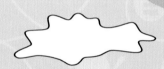

Squelch!

Look at that, on Igglepiggle's hand! Another mucky patch!

Don't worry Igglepiggle...
look who's coming.
It's Upsy Daisy.

Hello Upsy Daisy!

Upsy
Daisy!

Upsy Daisy gave
Igglepiggle a kiss.
And what do you
think happened?

Squelch!

Look at that, now Upsy Daisy
had a mucky patch on her tummy.

**Daisy
doo!**

Upsy Daisy held her friend
Igglepiggle's hand.

squelch!

And do you know... now
she had a mucky patch
on her hand, too.

Oh dear. Mucky patches **everywhere!**

Igglepiggle and Upsy Daisy decided
to go and see Makka Pakka.

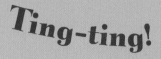

Ting-ting!

Here's the Ninky Nonk.

What a good idea,
to go by Ninky Nonk.

**Follow the
swoopy-swervy
Ninky Nonk trail
with your finger.**

The Ninky Nonk went up...

and the Ninky Nonk went down.

The Ninky Nonk went here...

and there... and all about.

The Ninky Nonk

What fun! And what a lot of mucky patches!

The Ninky Nonk stopped.
There was Makka Pakka,
with his soap and his sponge.

Ting-ting!

**Parp!
Parp!**

Makka Pakka blew his trumpet.
And what did he do next?

Makka Pakka took his soap
and his sponge.

Then Makka Pakka cleaned
off all those mucky patches.

Isn't that a pip?

**Makka
Pakka!**

Igglepiggle's mucky patch!

Colour Upsy Daisy and Igglepiggle. Draw some mucky patches on them!

Go to sleep, Igglepiggle.

Colour the sleepy stars above Igglepiggle in his boat.

Here are the Tombliboos.

Ombliboo Tombliboo
Knock on the door.

Ombliboo Tombliboo
Sit on the floor.

Ombliboo Tombliboo
Here is my nose –

Ombliboo Tombliboo
That's how it goes.

Draw over the dotted lines to complete the spots on the Tombliboos' trousers and colour them.

Hello Tombliboos!

Hello
Tombliboo
Unn.

Hello
Tombliboo
Ooo...

and hello
Tombliboo
Eee.

The Tombliboos' Busy Day!

Once upon a time in the Night Garden, the Tombliboos were riding in the Pinky Ponk.

Tombliboo! Tombliboo!

Through the window they saw...

the Haahoos. The Haahoos floated in the sky.

Ooo-ooo! said the Tombliboos. They were very pleased.
Haahoo! said the Haahoos.

Tombliboo! Tombliboo!

Bye-bye Haahoos! The Pinky Ponk stopped, and the Tombliboos got off.

What a lovely day the Tombliboos were having!
Now it was time to clean their teeth.
The Tombliboos found their toothbrushes, and they began.

Ombliboo, Tombliboo,
I can clean my teeth like you.
Tombliboos, form a line.
Scrub your teeth and make them shine.

Take your toothbrush, open wide
Up and down and side to side.
Round the back and underneath.
That's the way we clean our teeth!

What lovely clean teeth
the Tombliboos had.

They put their
toothbrushes back neatly.

What next?

Upsy Daisy!

Here comes Makka Pakka.
And here comes Upsy Daisy.
And here are the Pontipines!

Makka Pakka!

Mi-mi-mi-mi-mi!

What a lot of friends for the Tombliboos
to play with! What a busy day the
Tombliboos were having!

First the Tombliboos went
for a ride in the Pinky
Ponk. They cleaned their
Tombliboo teeth, and
they played in the garden.
What busy Tombliboos!

Isn't that a pip?

49

Tombliboos in the Pinky Ponk!

The Tombliboos are riding in the Pinky Ponk. Can you spot 4 differences in the bottom picture?

Answers: The red part of the wall is now pink; the Haahoo's face has changed colour; there is a spot missing on Unn's trousers; Eee has disappeared.

Go to sleep, Tombliboos.

Let's colour the Pinky Ponk!

The Tombliboos are fast asleep, and dreaming about riding in the Pinky Ponk.

Here are the Pontipines!

The Pontipines are friends of mine,
Although they're only small,
And even when there's ten of them,
They're hardly there at all.

Can you find 10 Pontipines hiding in this picture?

The Pontipines.

The Pontipines are a family of ten.

Mr and Mrs Pontipine,

four Pontipine boys...

and four Pontipine girls.

The Pontipine family live in a tiny house, next door to the Wottingers. The Pontipines like to wave to the Wottingers. The Wottingers wave back!

53

Hiding in the Flowerpots!

Once upon a time in the Night Garden, the teeny tiny Pontipines went out for a long walk.

They marched through the garden. One, two, three, four, five, six, seven, eight, nine, ten Pontipines, out for a walk.

Ten Pontipines marched up a tree.
They marched along a branch.
The Wottingers were marching along another branch.
The Pontipines waved to the Wottingers!

The Wottingers waved back.
The Pontipines waved back again.

The Pontipines love waving;
they were very pleased.
They turned to the children...

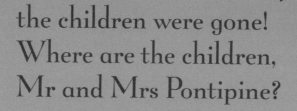

the children were gone!
Where are the children,
Mr and Mrs Pontipine?

The children were hiding.
Where do you think they were hiding?
Look at that.
Three handsome flowerpots.
A big one, a middle-sized
one and an ever so
little teeny tiny one.

The Pontipine
children were in the
tiniest flowerpot.

Mi-mi-mi-mi-mi-mi-mi-mi!

Mi-mi-mi-mi-mi-mi-mi-mi!

Now the Pontipine
children jumped
out of the tiny
flowerpot... into
the biggest one!

What fun.

Mr and Mrs Pontipine went home.

Soon it was time for the little Pontipines to go home too.
Do you know what they did?

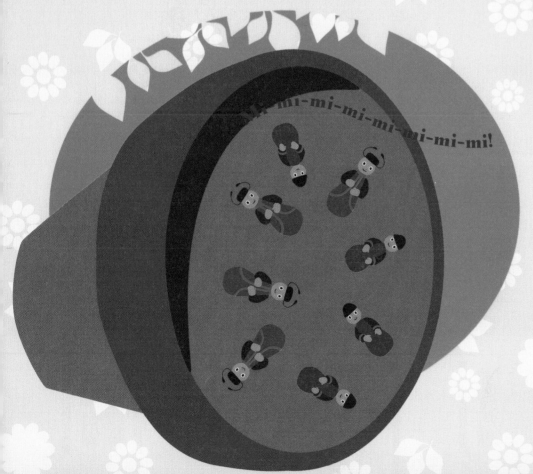

mi-mi-mi-mi-mi-mi-mi-mi!

The Pontipine
children rolled
all the way
home in the
big flowerpot!

The flower pot stopped outside the Pontipine house.

The Pontipine children bounced up out of the flowerpot! They flew up into the air, and down the chimney!

Mr and Mrs Pontipine kissed the children goodnight, and they all went to bed. One, two, three, four, five, six, seven, eight, nine, ten Pontipines, happy to be home.

Isn't that a pip?

Colour the Pontipine children.

Goodnight, Pontipines.

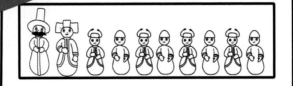

Colour the picture of the Pontipines tucked up in bed.

How many can you count? Write the number in the box.

Time to go to sleep everybody.

Go to sleep, Tombliboos.

Go to sleep, Upsy Daisy.

Go to sleep, Makka Pakka.

Go to sleep, Pontipines.

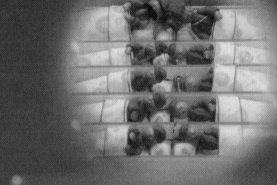

Go to sleep, Haahoos.

Go to sleep Ninky Nonk
and go to sleep, Pinky Ponk.

Wait a minute.
Somebody is not in bed!
Who's not in bed?
Igglepiggle is not in bed!

Don't worry, Igglepiggle...
it's time to go.